Classics *for*
Young Readers

TABLE OF CONTENTS

THE DOG AND HIS SHADOW

Once there was a big dog. When he got a bone he always hid it. He never gave a bit to any other dog.

If he saw a little dog with a bone he would say, "Bow-wow! Give me that bone!" Then he would take the bone.

One day he took a bone from a little dog. "The little dog shall not find this bone," he said. "I will take it far away. I will go across the brook and hide it."

So the big dog ran to the brook. There was a bridge over the brook. The dog ran out on the bridge. He looked down into the water and thought he saw another dog there. He thought the dog had a bone, too.

"I will take that bone," said the big dog. "Then I shall have two bones."

"Bow-wow!" said the big dog. When he did, his own bone fell out of his mouth. It fell into the brook. The big dog could not get it out.

There was not a dog in the water at all! The big dog has seen his own shadow.

THE GOOSE AND THE GOLDEN EGGS

There was once a man who had a goose. This goose was not like the geese you can find on a farm.

She was a very handsome goose, and every day she laid a big, golden egg. The man sold the eggs at the market. He saved the money and was slowly getting rich.

One day he said to himself, "I wish that I were rich now. Every day my goose lays a golden egg. She must have many golden eggs inside of her. If she has not, how can she lay golden eggs? If I could have all the gold at once I should be very rich." So the man killed his goose and tried to find the gold.

Alas! There was no gold to be found. The foolish man had lost the good that he had, without getting the riches that he wished.

THE GIRL AND THE MILK PAIL

A farmer's daughter was carrying a pail of milk on her head. As she walked, she began to think what she would do with the milk.

"I am going to sell this milk in the market. With the money I get for the milk, I can buy many eggs. When the eggs hatch, I will have lots of chicks. After the chicks grow into hens, I can sell them at the market."

The girl kept walking as she said to herself, "With the money I get for the hens, I can buy a new dress. I can wear my new dress to lots of parties. I will be the prettiest girl at the parties, and lots of men will ask me to marry them! But I will toss my head and say no to every one!"

At this thought, she tossed her head as she would do to the men. With that, the milk pail fell to the ground, spilling the milk and her dreams in the grass.

THE DOG AND THE WOLF

There once was a Wolf so skinny that he was nearly dead with hunger. He met a Dog who lived in a house in town.

The Dog saw the Wolf was near death. "Dear Wolf," said the Dog, "your wild life will be the end of you. Why not work as I do, and get your food given to you each day?"

"I would be willing to try anything," said the Wolf, "if I could just get a place to live and something to eat."

"I can take care of that for you," said the Dog. "Come with me to my master and you can share my work."

As the Wolf and Dog made their way to the town, the Wolf saw that the hair on the Dog's neck was worn very thin.

"Dear Dog," said the Wolf. "Why is the hair on your neck worn so thin that your skin shows?"

"Oh, it's nothing. Don't worry about that," said the Dog. "That is just the place where my master puts the collar on my neck each night. After supper, I am chained. You will get used to it."

"Is that what it costs to eat every day?" said the Wolf. "Then good-bye, Friend Dog. I would rather starve and be free."

THE FOX WITHOUT A TAIL

O nce there was a Fox who got his tail stuck in a trap. While trying to get away, he lost all his tail but a stump. At first, the Fox was ashamed to let his fellow foxes see him. But finally he came up with a way to make the other foxes look like him.

Calling all the foxes to a meeting, the Fox said, "Fellow Foxes, let me tell you how lucky I am to have lost my tail. In fact, I feel sorry for all of you. It is risky to have your tail flying in the wind when dogs are chasing you. And see how your tails get in the way when you sit down. Why don't you cut off your tails to make them short like my own stump?"

The foxes looked at each other and began to think their tails did get in the way. They were just getting ready to cut off each other's tails, when the Old Fox spoke.

"Our tails may cause us problems," said the Old Fox. "But I don't think you would tell us to cut them off if you hadn't lost yours!"

THE FOX AND THE GRAPES

One day a very hungry Fox came walking on a road. He spied a lush grape vine. The vine had large bunches of pretty purple grapes hanging down.

"Oh, those big grapes will make a fine lunch," said the Fox. He tried jumping to reach them, but the grapes were too high. He tried climbing the grape vine, but he kept falling off.

Then the Fox took a stick in his mouth and tried to bat the grapes down, but he could not hit them.

Now the Fox was tired and still hungry. "Well," he said, "I'm sure those grapes were sour and not ripe anyway." And he marched off in a huff.

THE BOY WHO CRIED "WOLF"

Once a little boy was sent to take care of a large flock of sheep.

His father said, "If a wolf comes to the pasture you must cry, 'Wolf! wolf!' Then the men who are working in the field will come and drive him away."

For many days no wolf came.

One day the little boy thought that he would have some fun. So he cried to the men, "Wolf! Wolf!"

"Where? Where?" cried the men, as they ran to the pasture.

The boy laughed and said, "There is no wolf. I called to you for fun."

The men went back to their work. They did not like the boy's fun.

Two or three times the boy called the men to the pasture. Each time the men ran to drive away the wolf and found no wolf there.

At last, one day, a wolf came to the pasture. "Help! Help! A wolf! A wolf!" cried the boy.

This time the men did not run to help him. They said, "He is having fun. We will not go."

The wolf killed one of the sheep and carried it to his den.

And the boy never called to the men in fun again.

THE TWO FROGS

Once upon a time there were two frogs who lived in Japan. One frog lived in Osaka near the sea. The other lived in Kyoto near a river. The two frogs had never met.

One day Osaka-frog said to his wife, "I am going to Kyoto. I wish to see the world."

On that same day Kyoto-frog said to his wife, "I am going to Osaka. I wish to see the world."

So one fine morning they both set out. They hopped along the same road. Kyoto-frog started from one end of the road, Osaka-frog from the other end.

Just half-way between the two towns was a mountain. It took a great many hops to get to the top. Kyoto-frog sang to himself, "Hop, hop, hop, I'll soon be at the top!" And there he was!

And there, in front of him, was another frog! He was so surprised he could not talk at first. Then the two frogs began to talk together. They found that they had both set out to see the world.

"I wish I were bigger," said Kyoto-frog. "Then I could see Osaka from here."

"I know what we'll do," said the other frog. "We will stand up on our hind legs and hold on to each other. Then we can each look at the town we are going to."

Kyoto-frog at once jumped up and put his front paws on his friend's shoulder. There they both stood. They held each other so that they would not fall down.

Kyoto-frog turned his nose toward Osaka. Osaka-frog turned his nose toward Kyoto.

They looked and looked, but the foolish frogs forgot one thing. Their great eyes were in the backs of their heads. Their noses pointed to the places to which they wanted to go. Their eyes looked at the places from which they had come.

"Dear me!" said Osaka-frog; "Kyoto is just like Osaka. It is not worth a trip. I am going home."

"Dear me!" said Kyoto-frog; "Osaka is just like Kyoto. It is not worth a trip. I am going home."

So they shook hands and set out for home again.

HOW THE ROBIN GOT ITS RED BREAST

O nce upon a time there was only one fire in the world. A man and a boy took care of it. They watched it all day and all night.

All the people in the world loved the fire. They could not live without it.

The white bear loved the cold and hated the fire. He watched the man and boy all day and all night. He hoped that sometime they would forget and let the fire go out.

One day when the boy was alone, he did forget. He went fast asleep and the fire was left with no one to watch it.

Then the white bear crept softly out of his hiding place. He jumped on the fire and rolled over and over on it until it was quite black.

"Good!" said the white bear. "Now I shall have peace."

"Chirp! Chirp!" sang a cheery voice. "Not if I know it!"

Out flew a gay little robin. He looked all around to be sure the bear was gone. Then he flew to the fire. Sure enough, there was one tiny spark left.

He began to fan the spark with his wings. The spark grew larger. More sparks came. Soon there was a blaze. The flames burned the robin's breast and turned it red, but he did not stop.

When the boy wakened, the fire was burning brightly, and a bird with a red breast was singing a gay little song.

THE UGLY DUCKLING

1

It was beautiful out in the country. It was summer. The cornfields were yellow and the oats were green. The hay was put up in stacks in the green meadows. Yes, it was beautiful out in the country.

A duck sat on her nest under the bushes. There were eggs in the nest, and she must hatch her young ones. At last one eggshell cracked, and then another. "Peep! Peep!" said the little ducks as they came out of the shells.

They looked all around them under the green leaves. The mother duck stood up and looked at her ducklings. Then she looked in the nest. There lay the largest egg of all. "How long must I sit here?" said the duck. "I am tired." But she sat down again.

"How are your ducklings?" asked an old duck who came to visit her.

"Look at them. Are they not the prettiest ducklings that you ever saw? They are all out but one. This egg will not crack."

"Let me see the egg," said the duck. "I think that it is a turkey's egg. Let it lie there, and teach your other children to swim."

"I think that I will sit on it a little longer," said the mother.

"As you please," said the old duck, and she went away.

At last the big egg cracked. "Peep! Peep!" said the little one as he came out of the shell. He was very large and very ugly.

The mother looked at him. "He does not look like the others," said she. "Can he be a turkey? We shall see. He must go into the water if I have to push him in myself."

The next day was bright and sunny. The mother duck went to the pond with her little ones. *Splash!* She jumped into the water. "Quack! Quack!" she said, and all the ducklings followed her. They swam about in the water. The ugly duckling swam with them.

"No, he is not a turkey," thought the mother. "How well he can swim! He is my own child."

"Quack! Quack!" she said. "Come with me to the farmyard. Keep near me and do not let the cat catch you."

So they came to the farmyard, and all the other ducks looked at them. "See that ugly duckling! We will not have him here," said one duck, and she flew up and bit him in the neck.

"Let him alone," said the mother. "He did not hurt you."

"Yes, but he is so large and ugly," said the duck who had bitten him.

"Your other children are very pretty," said the old duck. "Make yourself at home."

Now they were at home, but the duckling that came out of the big egg was bitten and laughed at by the ducks and chickens. "He is too big," they said.

The poor duckling was sad because he looked so ugly. At last he ran and hid in the bushes.

The little birds saw him and were afraid of him. "That is because I am so ugly," he thought. So he shut his eyes and flew far away over the fields.

2

At night the duckling came to a little hut. The door was open, and he went into the room. A poor woman lived in the hut with her cat and her hen. In the morning when they saw the duckling, the cat began to purr and the hen began to cluck.

"What is this?" said the woman. She could not see well and she thought it was a fat duck.

"Now," she said, "I shall have duck's eggs."

So the duckling lived in the hut three weeks, but no eggs came.

"Can you lay eggs?" asked the hen.

"No."

"Then do not talk to me," said the hen.

"Can you purr?" asked the cat.

"No."

"Then do not talk to me," said the cat.

At last one morning the duckling saw the sunshine and wished to swim on the water. He told this wish to the hen.

"What are you thinking of?" cried the hen. "You have nothing to do, that is why you think of such things. Purr, or lay eggs, and forget your silly wishes."

"But it is such fun to swim," said the duckling. "I like to put my head into the water and dive to the bottom of the pond."

"Yes, it must be fun!" said the hen. "What are you thinking of? Ask the cat about it. Ask him if he likes to swim, or to dive into the water."

"You do not understand me," said the duckling. "I think that I will fly out into the world again."

"Yes, do go," said the hen.

The duckling flew away to the water. He swam and dived, but he was not happy. No one liked him because he was so ugly.

3

Now came the autumn. The leaves in the forest turned yellow and brown. The wind played with them, and they danced over the ground.

One evening some beautiful birds came out of the bushes. They were as white as snow. They were swans. They flew high in the air and sailed away to the warm South.

The ugly duckling watched them. He did not know their names, but he loved them because they were so beautiful.

The winter was very, very cold. The poor duckling lived in the woods near the pond. He was often cold and hungry. It would be too sad if I were to tell you how unhappy he was.

At last spring came. The warm sun shone and the birds begin to sing. Then all at once the duckling could flap his wings. He flew high in the air and far away over fields and meadows. At last he came to a river in a beautiful garden. Three swans were swimming on the water.

"I will fly to them," said the duckling, "and they will kill me because I am so ugly. But what of that! It is better to be killed by them than to be bitten by the ducks and chickens in the farmyard."

So he flew into the water and swam toward the beautiful swans. They looked at him and came sailing down the river.

"Kill me," said the poor duckling, and he bent his head upon the water.

But what was this that he saw in the water! It was his own image. He was not an ugly duckling now. He was a beautiful white swan.

Some children came into the garden and threw bread and corn into the water. "There is a new swan!" cried one of the little girls.

The other children said, "Yes, a new one has come, and he is the most beautiful of all."

The old swans bowed their heads to him. Then the young swan hid his head under his wing, for he did not know what to do. He had always been called ugly, and now he heard the children say that he was beautiful.

"I never dreamed of being so happy," he thought, "while I was an ugly duckling."

Hans Christian Andersen

THE FISHERMAN AND HIS WIFE

A fisherman and his wife lived in a little old house by the sea. Every day the fisherman went down to the sea to fish. Every day his wife cooked the fish for dinner. One day, when he threw in his line, it suddenly became very heavy. He pulled and pulled, and out flopped a big fish. The fisherman said to himself, "This is too big for my wife and me. We will invite our friends to dinner."

But the fish said, "Oh, do not eat me. Put me back into the sea, and you shall have whatever you wish."

The fisherman quickly threw the fish back into the sea. "Who would eat a talking fish!" he said. "Go back to your friends, and I will throw my line for another fish." When he went back to his house, he told his wife about the talking fish.

"What a goose you are!" she said angrily. "Why did you not ask for something? Go back and ask him to change this shabby old house into a pretty cottage."

The fisherman walked slowly back to the sea. The water looked all yellow and green. The fisherman called:

"Oh, Man of the Sea,
Come listen to me,
For Ilsa, my wife,
The plague of my life,
Hath sent me to ask a gift
Of thee!"

The fish came swimming up to him.

"My wife wishes to live in a pretty little cottage," said the fisherman.

"Go home," said the fish. "She is in the cottage already."

The fisherman went home. Sure enough, there was his wife standing at the door of a pretty little cottage. The fisherman could hardly believe his eyes. There was a little garden in front and a chicken yard at the back.

"Ah! Now you shall be happy," said the fisherman.

And she was happy—for a week.

Then one day the wife said, "Husband, I am tired of this little cottage. It is too small. I wish to live in a big stone castle. Go to the fish and ask for one."

The fisherman walked slowly down to the sea. The water was dark and the sun did not shine. The fisherman called:

> "Oh, Man of the Sea,
> Come listen to me,
> For Ilsa, my wife,
> The plague of my life,
> Hath sent me to ask a gift
> Of thee!"

The fish came swimming up to him.

"My wife wishes to live in a big stone castle," said the fisherman.

"Go home," said the fish. "She is in the castle already."

The fisherman went home. Sure enough, there was a great stone castle. When the fisherman came to the door, it was opened by a servant, who made a low bow.

Inside the castle, he found more servants. And in the great hall he saw his wife. She was walking up and down, with her head in the air.

The fisherman rubbed his eyes and looked again. He saw golden chairs and tables and fine things to eat. He thought it must all be a dream.

"Wake up!" said his wife. "What are you staring at?"

"How grand it is!" said the fisherman. "Now you will be happy."

And happy she was—for a day.

The next morning, before the sun was up, Ilsa called to the fisherman, "Husband, go to the fish at once and tell him I wish to be queen of all the land."

The fisherman walked very slowly to the sea. The water was black and the waves rolled high. He called in a loud voice:

> "Oh, Man of the Sea,
> Come listen to me,
> For Ilsa, my wife,
> The plague of my life,
> Hath sent me to ask a gift
> Of thee!"

When the fish came swimming up to him, the fisherman said, "My wife desires to be queen of all the land."

"She is already queen," said the fish.

The fisherman hurried home and found his wife on a throne of gold and diamonds. She had a golden crown on her head, and wore a silk dress with a long train.

"Wife, wife, now you shall be happy," he said.

And happy she was—for an hour.

Then she said, "I am queen and you must do as I wish. I order you to go to the fish and tell him that I desire the power to make the sun and the moon rise and set whenever I choose."

The fisherman was very sad as he walked to the sea. The sky was full of black clouds. The waves were as high as hills. The thunder crashed and the fisherman had to shout:

"Oh, Man of the Sea,
  Come listen to me,
  For Ilsa, my wife,
  The plague of my life,
  Hath sent me to ask a gift
  Of thee!"

The fish rose on the top of a wave.

The fisherman said, "My wife wishes the power to make the sun and moon rise and set whenever she chooses."

"Go to your little old house," said the fish. "Remain there and be content."

And there you will find the fisherman and his wife to this very day.

The Three Wishes

There was once a poor woodcutter, who worked all day in the forest. He gathered great bundles of sticks and sold them in the village.

Once he had very bad luck indeed. No one wanted to buy any of his sticks. When the night came he had not a cent to take home to his wife.

"Dear me!" said the poor woodcutter. "No supper for us tonight!"

Just then he heard a strange noise in the dead leaves near the path. He turned to look and saw a rabbit caught in a trap.

"Here is supper," cried the old man, and ran to the trap.

"If you spare me," cried the rabbit, "I will grant the first three wishes made by you or your good wife."

"That is better than one supper," said the woodcutter, and he opened the trap.

The rabbit ran off into the forest, and the happy woodcutter hurried home to tell the good news to his wife.

She met him at the door of the hut. "What have you brought for supper?" she said.

"Nothing!" said the old man.

"Then there is nothing at all to eat," she wailed. "Oh, I wish I had a cake as big as a cart wheel!"

At once a cake appeared on the table. Such a large cake they had never seen.

"Wife, wife! What have you done?" cried the man. "We had three wishes. You have used one of them for a cake. I wish it were hung from your nose."

As he spoke, the cake rose slowly and stuck to the old woman's nose. The poor woodcutter was surprised. He pulled, but the cake stuck fast.

"Oh dear! Oh dear! Take it away!" cried the woman, but there it stayed.

"Never mind," said the woodcutter. "We have one more wish. Let us ask for all the riches in the world."

"But my nose!" cried the woman. "What is gold to me, while I have this great cake on my nose?"

"Hush!" cried the old woodcutter, but his wife would not hush.

Then the woodcutter became angry. "Away with the cake!" he shouted. "I wish it would fly up the chimney!"

Before the old man had said it, the big cake rolled from its place, and then flew up the chimney. A few crumbs rattled in the ashes, and that was the end of the three wishes.

THE JACKALS AND THE LION

Lion: I am hungry. I must find something to eat for my dinner. Gr-r-r-r-r! Where can all the animals be? I shall look till I find one. Gr-r-r-r-r!

Mother Jackal: Do you hear that lion roaring?
I am afraid he will eat us today. He has eaten all the other animals in the forest, and now he is looking for us, I know.

Father Jackal: Don't be afraid. I will take care of you. Let us run away from here. Come quick, quick, quick!

[The two little jackals run here and there looking for a place to hide.]

Lion: Gr-r-r-r-r!

Mother Jackal: Do you hear that roar again? I am so frightened. He will be sure to find us and kill us at once. What shall we do?

Father Jackal: He will not find us. We will hide till he goes back to his den. Then we will go to see him and talk to him about it.

Mother Jackal: Oh, we must not go near him! He will be sure to eat us if we do.

Father Jackal: No, he will not eat us. I'll see to that. He is not roaring now, so he must have gone back to his den. Come, we will go to him, and I'll show you what we can do.

[The two jackals go to the lion's den. The lion sees them coming and begins to roar.]

Lion: Who is this I see coming to my den? Gr-r-r-r-r-r! It is those two little jackals, and I have been hunting for them for three days. Gr-r-r-r-r! Where have you been hiding all the time? Didn't you know that I have been hunting for you? Come to me at once. I shall eat you for my dinner today.

Father Jackal: O great Lion, we know we should have come to you sooner than this, but there is a much bigger lion than you in the forest. He tried to catch us and eat us, and we were so frightened we had to run away.

Lion: What do you mean? There is no lion in this forest but me.

Father Jackal: Oh, yes, there is. And he is much bigger and more terrible than you.

Lion: That can't be true. Take me to this lion at once and I will take care of him.

Father Jackal: Follow us, then, and we will take you to this terrible lion. See! That is where he lives. Look down into that well and you will see him. He looks like you.
[The lion looks down into the well and thinks he sees another lion.]

Lion: What are you doing down there? I am the only lion that has any right in this forest. Come out of there! Gr-r-r-r-r! Come out, I say! If you do not come out, I shall jump down there and that shall be the end of you.
[The lion jumps down into the well. Soon he begins to roar. The jackals peep into the well.]

Jackals: Ho! Ho! Ho! Old lion! It was only yourself that you saw in the well. You may roar all you please, but you can't eat any more little jackals.

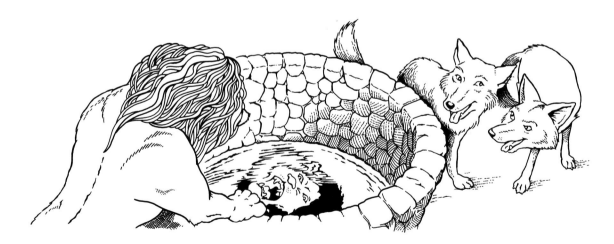

THE HOUND AND THE HARE

A Hound startled a Hare near the woods and began to chase her. As the Hare ran back and forth, the Hound played a game. At first, he bit her with his teeth as if he would end her life. Then he tumbled her in the grass as if playing with another dog.

Finally, not knowing whether she would be eaten or be the Hound's friend, the Hare stopped running.

She said, "Hound, I wish you would act truthfully with me. If you are my friend, why do you bite me? And if you are my enemy, why do you play with me?"

THE LION AND THE FOX

A lion who was old and weak could not go out to hunt for food. He went into his den and made believe that he was very sick.

Many animals went into the den to look at him. When they came near, he caught them and ate them.

After a great many had been caught in this way, a fox came along. He sat down outside the den and asked the lion how he was.

The lion said that he was very sick, and he begged the fox to come in and see him.

"I would," said the fox, "but I notice that all the footprints point into your den, and that none point out."

THE BREMEN TOWN MUSICIANS

Once there was a poor Donkey. He had worked hard all his life. But he had grown very old, and had become useless.

One day he heard his master say that he was a useless old Donkey, and must be killed very soon.

"I'll not stay here to be killed," said the Donkey. "I'll run away."

So he jumped over the fence and went down the road till he met a Dog.

"Where are you going, Mr. Dog?" asked the Donkey.

"I have run away," said the Dog. "They say that I am too old to work, and that they will have me killed. I will not stay to be killed."

"Right! Right!" said the Donkey. "Come with me, my good friend. You and I will go to Bremen town, and we will play in the band. You can play the flute, and I can beat the drum."

So the Donkey and the Dog went on together. By and by they met a Cat.

"How do you do, Mrs. Puss?" said they. "Where are you going?"

"I am running away," said the Cat. "My master and my mistress say that I am too old to catch mice, and that I shall have to be drowned. I will not stay to be drowned."

"Come with us," said the Donkey. "We are going to Bremen town to play in the band. You shall sing."

"That will suit me very well," said the Cat. So they all walked on.

By and by the three came to a farm. There on a fence stood a Cock, crowing as loud as he could.

"What ails you?" asked the Donkey. "Why do you crow so loud?"

"The cook says that I must go into the soup pot," answered the Cock. "So I will crow while I can, and as loud as I like."

"Why not come with us?" said the Donkey. "We are going to Bremen town, to play in the band. You can sing beautifully. Come with us. What do you say?"

"I will join you," said the Cock. So they all went on together.

It was now quite dark, and the four began to look about for a place to spend the night. "Let us sleep under this tree," said the Donkey.

So the Donkey and the Dog lay down on the ground. The Cat climbed into the tree, and the Cock flew up to the top.

"I see a light," cried the Cock. "There is a house not far away."

"Let us ask the people for supper," said the Donkey.

"How good a bone would taste!" said the Dog.

"Or a fat mouse," said the Cat.

"Or some corn," said the Cock.

They set out at once to the place where they saw the light. At last they reached the house. The Donkey, being the tallest, looked in the window.

"What do you see?" asked the others.

"I see a table with supper on it, and there are four robbers eating and drinking."

"Come down," said the Dog, "and we will think of a way to get that supper."

So they thought of a plan to frighten the robbers away. And this is what they did.

The Donkey stood on his hind legs, and placed his fore feet on the window sill.

The Dog climbed up and stood on the Donkey's back.

The Cat jumped up and stood on the Dog's back.

And the Cock flew up and stood on the Cat's back.

Then all together they began to make their loudest music.

The Donkey brayed, the Dog barked, the Cat mewed, the Cock crowed. They made such a noise that the robbers left their supper and ran away as fast as possible. Then the four friends sat down and ate the supper. "Now," said the Donkey, "let us all go to bed."

So the Donkey lay down in the yard, the Dog slept behind the door, the Cat curled up by the fire, and the Cock flew up on the roof. They were all so tired that they soon fell fast asleep.

About midnight the robbers saw that the light was out, and that all was still. So one of them crept back to the house. As he went to the fire to strike a light, the Cat flew at him and scratched him with her long nails. This frightened him so much that he ran back to the door. As he passed by, the Dog bit him in the leg. As he ran through the yard, the Donkey kicked him so hard that he was flung into the road. All this woke the Cock, who cried with all his might, "Cock-a-doodle-doo."

The robber ran back to his friends. "There was a wicked old witch sitting by the fire," he said. "She scratched me with her nails! Behind the door there was a man. He had a long, sharp knife, and he stabbed me in the leg! In the yard there was a giant, who kicked me out into the road! And then there was somebody who kept calling and calling, 'Kill the robber, do! Kill the robber, do!'"

So the robbers went away again as far as they possibly could, for they were very much afraid. And the four friends stayed in the little house in the woods and for all that you and I know, they are there now.

RUMPELSTILTSKIN

A miller had one daughter, of whom he was very proud. One day he boasted to the king that she could spin straw into gold.

"Send the girl to the palace at once. I should like to try her skill," ordered the king.

The daughter of the miller was sent to the king's palace. The king led the frightened girl into a large room filled with straw. Then he gave her a spinning wheel.

"You shall spin all night," said he. "If you do not spin all this straw into fine gold, you shall surely die tomorrow morning."

The king closed the door and left the miller's daughter alone in the room. The poor girl began to cry. "Oh, dear father," she cried, "why did you ever boast that I could spin straw into gold? Is there no help for me?"

Suddenly the door opened. A little elf with a hat walked into the room. "What does this mean?" he said.

"The king has ordered me to spin all this straw into gold, and I do not know how," the miller's daughter replied.

"What will you give me if I do it for you?" asked the elf.

"I will give you my necklace," said the miller's daughter.

The elf took the necklace. Then he seated himself at the wheel and worked busily all night.

Before sunrise the king returned. The straw had been spun into gold. The king took all of it, but he wished to have still more. The next night the king led the girl to a larger room, filled with straw. Once more he gave her a spinning wheel.

"Spin this straw into gold," he said, "or you shall die tomorrow morning." The king closed the door behind him, and the miller's daughter began to cry. At once the door opened, and the elf appeared.

"What will you give me this time if I spin the straw into gold?" the elf asked.

"I will give you my new ring," said the miller's daughter.

In the morning the king was happy when he saw the shining gold, but he wanted still more. That very night he led the poor girl to a larger room, filled with straw. "If you spin the straw into gold, you shall be my queen," he said. Then he left her alone in the room.

Again the little elf appeared. "If I spin all this straw into gold, what will you give me?" he said.

"I have nothing left to give you," the girl answered softly.

"Then promise, after you are queen, to give me your first child."

The girl did not know what to say. At last she said, "I will."

Again the straw was spun into gold, and on the very next day, the daughter of the miller married the king.

Years passed, and she was so happy that she forgot her promise to the elf.

One day she was holding her baby, when the old elf appeared in the room. Then she remembered.

"Oh, I cannot!" the poor queen cried. "I cannot part with my dear baby!"

"Guess my name," said the little elf, "and I will not take your child."

Then the queen sent her servants everywhere, to seek for strange names, but they could not find the right one.

One night as a page was walking through a forest, he saw a small fire burning brightly. An elf was dancing around the fire, and as he danced, he sang:

> *"Today I bake;*
> *Tomorrow I brew;*
> *Then, little prince,*
> *I come for you!*
> *For no one knows,*
> *Though great my fame,*
> *That Rumpelstiltskin*
> *Is my name!"*

The page ran back and told the queen.

"I am sure that is the same elf," said the queen.

The elf came to the palace two days later. "If you do not guess my name today, I will take your baby," he said.

"You cannot take him," the queen said. "Your name is Rumpelstiltskin."

Then the elf was oh so angry. He tore his hair and stamped upon the ground so hard that his feet stuck fast. "A fairy told you that!" he cried.

The queen laughed and went away. The elf tried to follow her. He pulled and pulled, but there he stuck. There are some who say he stands there still.

MAYOR RAT'S NIECE

Brown Rat lived with her uncle. Her uncle was Mayor of Ratville. Brown Rat was loved very much for her beauty and her pleasing ways.

Mr. Gray Fur lived in Ratville. He saw how pretty Brown Rat was, and he wished to marry her.

Every day he would call at her home and leave grains of wheat and other treats that rats like.

This made Mayor Rat very angry. One morning he said to his wife, "Gray Fur shall not marry our niece. Our beautiful Brown Rat must marry the greatest person in the whole, wide world. The sun, high up in the sky, gives us heat and light. The sun must be the greatest person in the whole, wide world. Perhaps he will marry our niece."

So the Mayor left Ratville and climbed up the blue sky until he met the sun.

"O Sun," cried Mayor Rat, "surely you, with your warm rays, must be the greatest person in the whole, wide world. Please marry my niece, Brown Rat."

"Ha, ha!" laughed the sun. "You are very much mistaken. I am not so great as you think. Do you see that cloud over there? He is much greater than I. He can make me hide my face."

Then Mayor Rat left the sun and traveled till he met the cloud floating along in the blue sky.

"O Cloud," said Mayor Rat, "surely you, who can hide the sun, must be the greatest person in the whole, wide world. Please marry my niece, Brown Rat."

"Ha, ha!" laughed the cloud. "You are very much mistaken. Indeed I am not the greatest person in the whole, wide world. Do you hear North Wind blowing? He is much greater than I. I go where he sends me."

Then Mayor Rat left the cloud and traveled till he met North Wind.

"O North Wind," said Mayor Rat, "you must be the greatest person in the whole, wide world. Please marry my niece, Brown Rat."

"Ha, ha!" laughed North Wind. "You are very much mistaken. I am not the greatest person in the whole, wide world. Do you see the strong wall around your garden? He is much greater than I. I cannot make him move, no matter how hard I blow."

Then Mayor Rat left the wind and climbed down from the sky. He walked and walked along until he came to the strong wall.

"O strong Wall," said mayor Rat, "you, whom the wind cannot move, must be the greatest person in the whole, wide world. Surely you will marry my niece, Brown Rat."

"Ha, ha!" laughed the wall. "You are very much mistaken. I am not the greatest person in the whole, wide world. Mr. Gray Fur, who lives in Ratville, is much greater than I. He can gnaw and make me fall. He must be the greatest person in the whole, wide world."

Beautiful Brown Rat was sitting in the garden. She heard what the wall had said to her uncle, Mayor Rat.

It made Brown Rat very happy to hear about Mr. Gray Fur.

She did not wish to marry the sun, although he gave light and heat.

She did not wish to marry the cloud, although he could hide the sun.

She did not wish to marry the wall, although strong North Wind was unable to move him.

She did wish to marry Mr. Gray Fur.

So Mr. Gray Fur and Brown Rat were married and lived happily, in a pretty little cottage next to the house of Mayor Rat.

THE GRASSHOPPER AND THE ANT

SCENE 1 – SUMMER

A Pleasant Field

Grasshopper: Ah, I am glad I have nothing to do! I can sit in the sun and be as lazy as I wish. I can watch the butterflies flit about on their pretty, bright wings, and I can listen to the humming of the bees. If I get hungry, there are juicy leaves to eat. If I get sleepy, I can hide in the grass and take a nap.

[Sings]
"The summertime's the time for me,
For then I'm happy as can be.
I watch the butterflies and bees;
I smoke my pipe and take my ease.
I do no work the livelong day;
I pass the time in fun and play.
Oh, summertime's the time for me!
For then I'm happy as can be."

[An ant comes along.]

Hello, Mr. Ant! Where are you going so fast?

Ant: About my work, of course. I'm a busy ant, I am.

Grasshopper: Oh, you are, are you? Well, you needn't be so cross about it.

Ant: Did I speak crossly? I didn't mean to. I'm sorry. But I am very busy and can't stop to talk. *[Starts to go.]*

Grasshopper: Wait, wait! You can take time to talk a minute, can't you?

Ant: Why, yes, if you really have something to say.

Grasshopper: Ha, ha! You make me laugh. Can't you stop a while to talk with your friends, even if they haven't much to say?

Ant: I have no time to waste.

Grasshopper: Why, what are you doing today?

Ant: I am very busy getting ready for winter.

Grasshopper: Getting ready for winter! Why, winter is a long way off!

Ant: It will be here soon enough.

Grasshopper: Well, I don't see why you don't have a good time while you can.

Ant: But if I don't gather food for the winter now, while there is plenty of it, I shall not have anything to eat when cold weather comes.

Grasshopper: Oh, you are a dull fellow! You have no fun in you.

Ant: I don't work all the time. I am busy all day, but when evening comes, I sit at home and talk with my friends.

Grasshopper: Well, I don't mean to work at all in this fine weather. I'm going to have a good time.

Ant: Wait till winter comes, and we shall see who is wiser—you or I. Good-bye, I have work to do. *[Goes on.]*

Grasshopper: What a foolish fellow that ant is! He does nothing but work, work, work. He doesn't have any fun at all. Well, I don't care. I am going to have a good time.

[Sings]

"The summertime's the time for me,
For then I'm happy as can be.
I hop about among the flowers;
I sing and dance for hours and hours.
I care not what the ant may say;
The summertime's the time for play.
Oh, summertime's the time for me!
For then I'm happy as can be."

SCENE 2 – WINTER

[In Front of the Ant's House]

Ant: [Looking out of the window.] Ah, it's a cold day! I'm glad I don't have to go out. I can stay cozily at home and talk with my friends. I have plenty of food, too, so I have nothing to do through the winter but have a good time.

*[Grasshopper comes along. He looks thin and hungry.
His clothes are old and ragged. He stops in front of
the ant's house.]*

Grasshopper: Oh, Mr. Ant, won't you please give me something to eat?

Ant: Why, Mr. Grasshopper? Is that you? I hardly knew you. You are not looking very well.

Grasshopper: No, no! I'm afraid not. I'm not feeling well, either.

Ant: Why, what's the matter?

Grasshopper: I am hungry. Won't you please give me something to eat?

Ant: Something to eat! Why, what did you do all summer?

Grasshopper: I sang and played all summer. I had plenty of food then. Now it is cold, and there is nothing to eat.

Ant: Oh, you lazy fellow! You sang and played all summer, while the rest of us were busy storing up food for the winter. Now that it is cold and there is no food, you ask us to feed you. Take this grain, but do not ask again. You shall get no more from me.

Grasshopper: Ah, me! Why did I not work as the ant did, and store up food while there was still food to get?

[Sings sadly] "I did no work all summer long.
And now I know that I was wrong.
It isn't right for me to play
While the ants work hard all day.
Next time I'll work as well as dance,
Then I'll be ready, like the ants."

THE FOOLISH GOOSE

Characters:

**GRAY GOOSE · WISE OLD CROW · WHITE CRANE ·
BROWNIE HEN · A FARMER**

TIME: One Bright Morning   **PLACE:** A Big Road

[Gray Goose goes walking down the road, with a bag of corn—very proud and happy. He meets Wise Old Crow.]

Wise Old Crow: Good morning, Gray Goose! What a heavy bag you have there! It is too much for you to carry alone. Let me help you.

Gray Goose: Oh, no! It is a big bag of corn, but I can carry it without any help.

Wise Old Crow: Oh, well, I just wanted to help you as a friend. How long do you think your bag of corn will last you? I can tell you of a plan to make a little corn go a long way.

Gray Goose: What is your plan? Tell me how to make my corn go a long way, Wise Old Crow.

[He puts down his bag of corn in the road.]

Wise Old Crow: First, you must spread your corn out on the ground, so that we can count it. Then, you count on one side and I will count on the other side.

[Gray Goose takes some of the corn out of the bag and spreads it on the ground.]

Gray Goose: [Counting.] One, two, three, four, five, six, seven, eight, nine—

Wise Old Crow: [Eating a grain of corn each time he counts.] One, two, three, four, five, six, seven, eight, nine—

Gray Goose: [Looking up.] What are you doing, Wise Old Crow? Stop eating my corn!

Wise Old Crow: [*As he flies away, laughing.*] Caw! Caw! Caw! I told you that I knew a plan to make a little corn go a long way!

[*Gray Goose picks up his bag of corn, which is not so heavy now, and goes along the road. After a while he meets White Crane.*]

White Crane: Good morning, Gray Goose! What do you have in your bag?

Gray Goose: Oh, that is some of the best corn in the world.

White Crane: Is that all? You carry it with such care that I thought it must be pearls or diamonds.

Gray Goose: No, I've never seen any pearls or diamonds. I should like very much to see such sights!

White Crane: Well, just swim out to that big rock in the lake over there. The bottom of the lake is covered with beautiful pearls and diamonds. I will keep your corn for you.

[Gray Goose swims out to see the wonderful sights. While he is gone White Crane eats nearly all of the corn. Gray Goose cannot see any pearls or diamonds on the bottom of the lake. When he starts back, he sees White Crane eating the corn.]

Gray Goose: Go away from my corn, White Crane! Go away from my corn!

White Crane: [As he flies off, laughing.] I told you that I would keep your corn for you, Gray Goose!

[Gray Goose picks up the little corn that is left, and goes down the road. After a while he meets Brownie Hen and her ten chicks.]

Brownie Hen: What have you got in that little bag, Gray Goose?

Gray Goose: Oh, just a few grains of corn. I had a big bag full, but White Crane ate most of it while I was looking for pearls and diamonds! I like to see strange sights.

Brownie Hen: Well, if you like to see strange sights, throw your corn upon the road and see what happens.

Gray Goose: No, indeed! I know well enough what

would happen! Your ten little chicks would eat every grain of it.

Brownie Hen: No, no, Gray Goose! My chicks will not steal your corn. Throw some of it upon the road. If my little ones eat a single grain, I will give you ten white eggs.

Gray Goose: All right! I agree to that.

[He throws down some corn. The chicks run toward it. But before they can eat it, Brownie Hen makes a noise like a hawk. The chicks run away, and Brownie Hen eats the corn.]

Brownie Hen: I told you that my chicks would not eat your corn, Gray Goose!

[Gray Goose goes on until he meets a Farmer.]

Farmer: What is in your bag, Gray Goose?

Gray Goose: [Sadly.] Only a few grains of corn. My bag grows smaller and smaller. I wish I could make it grow bigger and bigger!

Farmer: Why don't you put the corn in the ground? Then it will grow, and you will always have plenty to eat.

Gray Goose: I will do as you say, Farmer.

[He plants it, and later the corn begins to grow. For every grain he planted, Gray Goose has hundreds of grains!]

Gray Goose: At last I have found a way to make my bag of corn grow bigger and bigger instead of smaller and smaller!

LITTLE RED RIDING HOOD

A little girl once lived in a cottage near a great forest. She often wore a long red cloak and a little red hood. For this reason, she was always called Little Red Riding Hood.

No other children lived very near her. Little Red Riding Hood often played alone in the forest with the animals and birds. Even the shy little rabbits came to eat carrots from her hand.

One day her mother called to her, "Come here, Little Red Riding Hood."

"Yes, mother," said the little girl.

She found her mother at the door, with a basket in her hand. "Your Grandmother is not well," said her mother. "I want you to take her this basket of butter and cakes. Follow the path through the forest. Be sure not to stop to play, and be very sure not to talk to the wicked wolf."

Red Riding Hood ran down the path. Soon she saw some red berries. "Grandmother always likes these," she thought, and began to pick them. As she did so, the big gray wolf came from behind a tree. Red Riding Hood did not see him. "Good morning," said the big wolf. "May I help you pick berries?"

Red Riding Hood forgot all about what her mother had told her.

"Yes, indeed," she cried. "I want to fill the whole basket and take it to my Grandmother."

"Where does your Grandmother live?" asked the wolf while he picked berries.

"Down at the end of this path," said Red Riding Hood.

The wolf laughed aloud and showed his teeth. Then he ran away. He ran until he reached the house where the Grandmother lived. There he knocked at the door.

"Who is there?" cried Grandmother.

"Only Little Red Riding Hood," said the wolf.

"Come in, dear," said Grandmother. The door opened and the wolf came in. When Grandmother saw the big wolf, she forgot that she was sick, and ran through the forest. When she was gone, the wolf put on her cap and dress and climbed into bed.

Very soon Red Riding Hood tapped at the door.

"Come in, my dear," said the wolf.

Red Riding Hood entered the room. "Good morning, Grandmother! Here are some cakes and berries for you," said the little girl.

"Put them on my table," said the wolf. "I am glad you have come, for I am very hungry."

Red Riding Hood came nearer.

"Grandmother, what large eyes you have!" she said to the wolf.

"The better to see you, my dear!"

"What long arms you have!"

"The better to hug you, my dear!"

"But Grandmother, why are your teeth so sharp?"

"So that I may eat you, my dear!" cried the wicked wolf. He sprang out of the bed and ran toward the little girl. Red Riding Hood cried out.

Suddenly the door opened, and then Grandmother rushed in with some men from the forest. The gray wolf ran out of the house with the men after him. They did not catch him, but they did not stop running until he was far away.

As for our Little Red Riding Hood, she very often played in the forest, but she never talked to a wolf again.

THE STEADFAST TIN SOLDIER

"Tin soldiers! Tin soldiers!" cried a little boy clapping his hands. There were twenty-five of them in the box, and they had been given to him for his birthday. Now he took them from the box and set them one by one on the table. They were all just alike except one. This poor fellow had only one leg, but he stood as firmly on this one leg as the others did on their two. And he is the hero of our story.

The little box had many other presents for his birthday. On the table in front of the Tin Soldier was a beautiful castle. There were trees around it, and in its door stood a little paper lady. She was dancing. She stretched out her arm and lifted one leg in the air. The Tin Soldier thought that she had only one leg like himself. "She would be just the wife for me," he thought, "but she lives in a castle and must be of high rank. Still, I should like to know her." So he hid behind a basket where he could watch the paper maiden.

At night all the other soldiers were put away into the box. The little boy went to bed, and then his birthday playthings began to play. They ran and jumped and fought. The tin soldiers rattled in their box, for they wanted to get out and join in the sport. The only playthings that did not move were the Tin Soldier and the dancing maiden. She remained standing on the toe of one foot with her arms outstretched. He stood firmly on his one leg, and his eyes never turned from her.

The clock struck twelve. Crash! Off flew the lid of a box at the Tin Soldier's elbow! Out jumped a little imp! "Tin Soldier," said the imp, "keep your eyes to yourself."

The Tin Soldier never turned his head. "Well, only wait till tomorrow," said the imp.

The next morning the little boy placed the Tin Soldier on the windowsill, far away from the little dancer. Suddenly the window blew open. The Tin Soldier fell to the ground, three stories below. He landed on his head with his gun sticking into the ground. His one leg pointed straight up.

The little boy came running out of the house to find the lost soldier. He looked and looked but could not see him. If the Tin Soldier had cried, "Here I am," the boy would have found him. "But soldiers never cry," thought the brave Tin Soldier.

It now began to rain. There was a heavy shower. The water ran in the streets. When the shower was over, two boys came by.

"Look," said one, "here is a tin soldier. Let us give him a sail in a boat."

So they made a boat out of an old letter and put the Tin Soldier into it. Away he sailed down the gutter. The boys ran along beside him, clapping their hands. The paper boat rocked to and fro, until the Tin Soldier was dizzy. Still he did not move but stood firmly on his one leg, looking straight ahead and clasping his gun.

All at once the boat sailed into a tunnel under the pavement. "Good bye, Tin Soldier," cried the boys.

It was as dark in the tunnel as in the tin box. "Where shall I go next?" thought the Tin Soldier. "Is this what the imp meant when he said, 'Wait till tomorrow'? If only the little dancer were with me, I should not care even if it were twice as dark."

Just then a great water rat swam toward the boat.

"Stop!" it cried. "Where is your passport?"

But the Tin Soldier was silent and held his gun with a still firmer grasp. The boat sailed on, and the rat followed. The stream flowed more swiftly. The boat came out from the tunnel, and the Tin Soldier saw the bright daylight. Then he heard the roaring noise of a

waterfall. The boat rushed forward. It spun round and round. It filled with water. It was ready to sink. The brave Tin Soldier did not even wink. He stood still and stiff while the water rose up to his neck, and over his head. He thought of the paper dancer. "Farewell, dear lady," said he.

The paper boat was torn in two. The Tin Soldier felt himself sinking. Just then he was swallowed by a large fish.

How dark it was, darker than in the tin box, darker than in the tunnel. The Tin Soldier was as brave as ever. He lay quiet for a long, long time, still holding his gun.

Then it was light again and someone cried, "The Tin Soldier!" The fish had been caught and taken to the kitchen. The cook had cut it open and found the Tin Soldier.

He was taken into the playroom and put upon the table. Can you believe it? He was in the very same room where he had been before. There were many children about. Everyone came to look at him, the wonderful soldier who had been swallowed by a fish.

The Tin Soldier stood up straight on his one leg. There were the other playthings. There was the fine castle. There was the pretty dancer standing on one leg while she held the other leg high in the air. He could have cried with joy, but soldiers do not cry. He looked at the dancing lady. She looked at him. Neither spoke a word.

Now one of the little boys took the Soldier and threw him into the stove. What made the boy do this? No doubt the imp in the box had something to do with it. The Tin Soldier felt himself growing hot and beginning to melt. Once again he looked at the little dancer.

A door opened, and a breeze blew into the room. The wind caught the maiden, and she flew across the room straight to the Tin Soldier. They both flamed up in the blaze and were gone.

When the servant took out the ashes the next morning, he found a little lump of tin in the shape of a heart.

Hans Christian Andersen

THE MAN AND HIS DONKEY

Man: Come, my son, we will take this donkey to market this morning and sell him. He is not of much use to us now, and I need the money more than I need him.

[The man and his son start out to the market, driving the donkey. When they have gone a little way, they meet a neighbor.]

Neighbor: How foolish you are to walk along the road and drive your donkey instead of riding him!

Man: I believe you are right, neighbor. I will have my son ride the donkey.

[He puts his son on the donkey, and they start on again. They soon meet another neighbor.]

Neighbor: Boy, how can you ride that donkey and let your poor old father go along on foot?

Man: It doesn't look right, my son. Get off and let me ride.

[They make the change and set out again.
They pass two men who stop and begin to
talk to each other about them.]
Men: Look at that big, strong man riding, while his poor little son follows after on foot. Why doesn't he take the boy up behind him?
Man: Do you hear what those men are saying, my son? Perhaps it would look better if you ride, too. Come, get up behind me.
[The boy gets on the donkey, and they go on again.
They soon meet another neighbor.]
Neighbor: Is that your donkey?
Man: Yes. Why do you ask?
Neighbor: No one would think so from the way you use him. You are better able to carry the poor donkey than he is to carry both of you.
Man: Then, my son, let us get off and carry the donkey.

[They get a pole and tie the donkey's legs to it.
Then each takes an end of the pole, and they go
on to market carrying the donkey. As they go through
the village, the people all stop and laugh at them.]

Village People: Ha! Ha! Ha! Ho! Ho! Ho! What a funny sight! A man and a boy carrying a donkey! Whoever heard of such a thing?

[The man becomes very angry. He puts down the donkey, unties him, and throws the pole away.]

Man: My son, we must do just what I thought best at first. You and I will walk, and we will drive the donkey before us. When we try to please everybody, we please nobody. And we will take the donkey home, as he has been the wisest of us all today.

LITTLE HALF-CHICK

O nce upon a time a hen hatched out some little chickens. She was very much pleased with their looks as they came out of their shells.

But when the last one came out it was only a half-chicken. It had only one leg, one wing, and one eye. It was just half a chicken.

The hen-mother did not know what to do with him. She was afraid something would happen to him, so she tried hard to keep him from harm.

But as soon as he could walk he began to be naughty. He would not mind, and he went wherever he wanted to go.

One day he said to this mother, "I am going to the city to see the king. Goodbye."

The poor hen-mother did not want him to go, so she said, "No, no, little Half-Chick, you must not try to go so far. You will be sure to come to harm."

But little Half-Chick said, "Yes, I am going to see the king. I do not like to stay here." And away he went over the fields.

When he had gone a little way, he came to a brook that was choked in the weeds. "Little Half-Chick, little Half-Chick," whispered the water, "these weeds are choking me. I cannot move, and I am almost lost. Please help me get the sticks and weeds away."

"I have no time for you," said Half-Chick. "I am going to the city to see the king." And away he went.

After he had gone a little way he came to a fire. It was dying under some damp sticks. "Oh, little Half-Chick, little Half-Chick," said the fire, "you are just in time to save me. I am almost dead for want of air. Please fan me with your wing."

"I have no time for you," said Half-Chick. "I am going to the city to see the king." And away he went.

After a time he came to a clump of bushes. The wind was caught in them and could not get away.

"Oh, little Half-Chick, little Half-Chick," said the wind, "you are just in time to help me. Please bend these bushes aside and let me get away."

"I have no time for you," said Half-Chick. "I am going to the city to see the king." And away he went.

He went on and on till he came to the city and then to the palace of the king. He went in at the gate and up the walk. Just then the cook looked out and saw him.

"The very thing for the king's dinner," she said. So she took the little Half-Chick and put him into a pot of water on the fire. The water came up over his head and into his eye. He cried out, "Oh, water, please don't drown me! Please don't come so high!" But the water said, "Little Half-Chick, you would not help me when I was in trouble." Then it came higher than ever.

The fire made it hotter and hotter. The little Half-Chick cried out, "Do not burn so hot, fire. You are burning me up. Please stop burning."

But the fire said, "Little Half-Chick, when I was in trouble you would not help me." Then it burned hotter than ever.

Soon the cook took the cover off to look at the dinner. "This chicken is no good," she said. "It is burned to a cinder."

So she took the little Half-Chick up by his leg and threw him out of the window. The wind took him up higher than the trees. It turned him round and round till he was so dizzy he thought he should die.

"Don't blow me so high, wind," he said. "Please let me go."

"Little Half-Chick," said the wind, "when I was in trouble you would not help me." So the wind blew him up to the top of the church steeple and stuck him there. He stands there to this day, with his one eye, his one wing, and his one leg. The wind whirls him round and round, and he keeps his head turned toward it to hear what it says.

KING MIDAS

1

Once upon a time there lived a very rich king, whose name was Midas. This king was very fond of gold. He loved it more than anything in the world.

King Midas had a little daughter named Marygold. When Marygold picked buttercups and dandelions, he used to say, "If these flowers were as golden as they look, I would pick them."

One day King Midas was in his treasure room counting his treasure. He looked up and saw a stranger in the room.

"You are a rich man, friend Midas," said the stranger.

"Yes, I have some gold," answered Midas. "But it is not enough."

"What!" cried the stranger. "Are you not happy?"

Midas shook his head.

"What would make you happy? What do you wish?"

King Midas thought and thought. At last he looked at the stranger and said, "I wish that everything I touch may turn to gold."

"Are you sure you would be happy then?"

"Yes," answered Midas. "I would ask for nothing more."

"It shall be as you wish," said the stranger. "Tomorrow at sunrise you shall have the Golden Touch."

2

When the sun peeped into the room, King Midas jumped out of bed.

He touched a chair. It turned to gold.

He touched the bed and the table, and they were changed to solid, shining gold.

He dressed himself, and all his clothes were gold.

Then King Midas went into his garden. "Now," he thought, "I can have the most beautiful garden in the world."

So he touched all the leaves and flowers, and they became shining gold.

When the King had done this he was hungry, so he went to the palace for his breakfast.

He tried to drink some water. When he touched it to his lips it turned into gold. He touched the fish on his plate. It became a pretty gold fish and he could not eat it.

He took an egg. That, too, turned into gold.

Just then Marygold ran to her father and put her arms about his neck. "Good morning, dear Father," she said.

The King kissed his little daughter. "My dear, dear Marygold," he cried. But Marygold did not answer.

Alas! What had he done! His dear daughter, his sweet little Marygold, was changed to gold by his kiss.

3

King Midas began to cry. Now, at last, he did not care for gold. His little daughter was dearer to him than all the gold in the world.

"How can I live without my dear Marygold?"

he thought. "I would give all my money if my little girl could come back to me."

Then the stranger came again. "Well, friend Midas," he said, "how do you like the Golden Touch?"

"I am very unhappy," said Midas. "I know now that gold is not everything."

"Let us see," said the stranger. "Which do you think is worth more—the Golden Touch, or a cup of water?"

"A cup of water!" cried the King.

"The Golden Touch, or a crust of bread?"

"Give me a crust of bread," answered the King.

"The Golden Touch, or your dear little Marygold?"

"Oh, my child, my dear child!" cried Midas. "She is worth more than all the gold in the world."

"Go, then, to the river at the foot of your garden," said the stranger. "The water in the river will take away the Golden Touch. Fill this pitcher with the water and sprinkle everything you have touched."

King Midas ran through the garden and jumped into the river.

Then he filled the pitcher and ran back to the palace. He sprinkled the water over the golden child, and she became his own little laughing, dancing Marygold once more.

CLYTIE

People long ago thought that gods and goddesses lived in the trees and brooks and flowers. One of the most beautiful of these goddesses was golden-haired Clytie.

Clytie was a water goddess that lived in a river near the great sea. She loved the sun god Apollo who drove the chariot of the sun.

Day after day Clytie stood on the bank of her river home and watched for Apollo's chariot to come up in the east. All day she stood and watched him driving across the sky. In the evening when the sun went down, she stood looking after him.

For nine long days she stood there. All that time she ate nothing but dewdrops, and every day she grew more pale and thin.

At last the gods took pity on her. They changed her into a beautiful flower.

Her feet became roots in the ground. Her body changed to a green stem, and her golden hair turned to yellow petals.

But Clytie still kept her face turned toward Apollo as he crossed the sky. So it came to pass that people named her Sunflower.

ECHO

Long, long ago, there lived a young girl named Echo. She was very bright and pretty, but she was very naughty, too.

She dearly loved to tease. She teased her mother, she teased her father, and she teased her brothers and her sisters. She played tricks on all the people she knew.

"You like to tease too much," her friends would say to her. "Some day you will be sorry."

But Echo would only laugh and go on with her tricks.

One day she was foolish enough to play a trick on the great Queen Juno. Queen Juno was very angry.

"After this you shall never speak to any one first," she said. "You shall only say again what others say to you."

Poor Echo! All her fun was gone. She could not speak to any one, but could only answer when she was called.

She grew thinner and thinner, and weaker and weaker. At last she faded away until she was only a voice.

Sometimes you can hear her now in the woods. She will not speak to you, but she will answer you back if you call.

Echo Echo Echo Echo Echo

ANDROCLES AND THE LION

Androcles was a slave. He lived with his master in Rome, many years ago. The master was a cruel man. Androcles did not have enough to eat, and he had to work very hard.

One night, Androcles ran away. He crept along until he was outside the city walls. Then he ran until he was tired. He lay down on the soft grass and went to sleep. In the morning, he looked around and saw that he was near a forest. He knew there were wild animals in the forest, but he thought the animals would be no more cruel to him than his master had been.

Androcles was very hungry. He ate some nuts and berries and drank some water from a spring. He found a dark cave in the rocks. He sat down in the cave and tried to plan what he would do next.

Suddenly, he saw a shadow across the low opening of the cave. He heard the roar of a wild animal.

Androcles was a brave man, but the roar frightened him. He tried to run away, but the animal filled the low opening.

Then Androcles saw that it was a lion. The great lion raised one paw and moaned with pain. He had a thorn in the soft part of his paw.

Androcles had often taken thorns out of the paws of his master's dogs. So he gently took the lion's paw in his hand. The lion sat very still while the thorn was being pulled out. Then he did just what the dogs had done. He rolled over and over in his joy.

He licked the hands of Androcles and tried to lick his face. When Androcles left the cave, the lion followed him. The lion was a good hunter and caught small game for him. They lived together in the cave and became good friends.

One day Androcles left the cave and walked by himself in the forest. Suddenly, he was seized by soldiers from Rome. His cruel master had sent them to hunt for him. They took him back to Rome. He was put into prison.

After many days, they took him out of prison. They took him to a large open place like a circus. There were seats on every side. The seats were full of cruel men and women. His master was there and his master's friends. They had come to see Androcles fight for his life with a hungry lion.

Androcles stood still, waiting for the lion. All the people watched and waited. The cage door was opened. Out rushed a hungry lion. Androcles was frightened but he did not move. On came the lion, but just as he reached Androcles, he stopped and sniffed the air. Then, with a joyous bound, he lay down at the feet of his old friend. Androcles stroked the head of the lion. The lion licked the hands and feet of Androcles.

All the people watched. There was not a sound in the great place. Then a cheer went up as they saw that Androcles and the lion were friends.

"Tell us about it," the people cried. So Androcles told his story. Then he waited. He thought the cruel people might make him fight another lion. But the people did not feel cruel now.

"Let them both go free!" they shouted. So Androcles and the lion went back to the forest together.

Pandora's Box

A long time ago there lived a maiden named Pandora. In those days every one was happy, for trouble and pain were not known.

Pandora should have been the happiest of all, for when she was born, the gods gave her all their gifts. She had health and good temper, and wit and beauty, and everything else that a maiden could wish.

But Pandora had one thing that did not make her happy. It was a beautiful wooden box tied with a golden cord. The king of the gods himself had given it to her.

"What good does it do me?" Pandora said to herself. "What good is a box tied up with a golden cord if you have been told never, never to open it?"

Now Pandora wished and wished and wished that she could know what was in the box. Every day she sat looking at it and wondering what could be inside it.

"What harm could it do?" she said to herself. "I would only peep in and close the lid quickly."

Once she thought she heard soft noises inside. That time she had her fingers on the cord. Then she suddenly remembered and stopped.

At last Pandora could stand it no longer and she opened the box. She thought she would just lift the lid and close it again quickly. But before she knew it, a swarm of ugly creatures flew out.

Then Pandora felt pain and sorrow for the first time in her life. With a cry, she dropped the lid of the box. But it was too late.

She had let loose the troubles of the world. They flew out through the window, carrying sorrow and pain everywhere.

Pandora was very much frightened. As she sat there wondering what she should do, she heard a sweet voice inside the box. "Pandora," it called. "Pandora, let me out. I am Hope, and I will help you."

Now Pandora did not know who Hope was, but the voice sounded so kind that she lifted the lid.

The little creature that came out this time was not a bit like the others. Her wings were like sunshine. It made Pandora feel better just to see her.

Of course Hope could not bring the ugly creatures back into Pandora's box. They flew through the world, carrying pain and sorrow where such things had never before been known.

But wherever they went, Hope went too, bringing comfort to all who were sick and sad. She is still in the world today, and happy are the people who have seen her wings.

PUSS IN BOOTS

A poor miller had three sons. When he died he left them all he had. To the oldest he left his mill. To the second he left his donkey. To the youngest he left his cat.

"What shall I do?" said the youngest. "My brothers can get on very well. They have the mill and the donkey. But I have only the cat. I wish I had silver and land."

But the cat purred and said, "Do not be sad, master. We shall do very well. Bring me a pair of boots to keep my feet from mud and briars, and get me a bag to carry. Then we'll see what can be done to get silver and land."

So he brought some fine large boots for his cat, and a green bag with a red string to it. Then Puss took the bag and some apples, and marched out among the briars. She put a red apple into the bag, and left it open on the ground. Then she lay down and made believe that she was asleep.

Soon a young rabbit came to the place. It smelled the apple and looked into the bag. Then it went in to get the apple.

Puss pulled the string and shut the bag. She took the rabbit to the King of the country, and said, "My master is the Marquis of Carabas. He sends you this rabbit."

The King took the rabbit, and said, "Tell your master I am much pleased."

Then Puss went into a field of corn, and sat with the bag open. Soon two young quails ran into it. Puss pulled the string and shut them in. She took these to the King, and said, "My master, the Marquis of Carabas, sends you these quails."

The King said, "Tell your master I am much pleased."

Every day for a month or more Puss took the King a present. And the King said every day, "Tell your master I am much pleased to receive this present."

One day Puss heard the King say he would go riding by the river. She told her master to go and swim in the river.

Soon the King rode by with a company of men. Puss went to meet him along the bank of the river and called, "Help! Help! My master will drown."

The King sent his men to help. They drew the young man to the bank.

"This is the Marquis," said Puss. The King liked the young man. He thanked him for all the presents, and told his men to bring dry clothes for the Marquis. Then the King asked the Marquis to ride in the coach between himself and his daughter.

Puss marched on before, in her boots. Soon she saw some men cutting grass. She spoke to them and said, "Tell the King that this land belongs to the rich Marquis of Carabas."

So when the King came near and asked, "Whose land is this?" they answered, "This is part of the land of the Marquis of Carabas. He is very rich."

Puss walked on before, in her boots. Soon she came to a giant's castle. She stepped in. She saw the giant. He was big and mean and terrible. She said, "They say you can change yourself into a lion, or a mouse, or anything. I do not think it is true. Can you show me?"

"Yes," said the angry giant, "I will show you that I can." Then he changed himself into a lion, and roared so loud that he almost broke the windows. Puss was so frightened that she ran clear up to the roof.

When she came down and peeped into the room, there sat the giant. "That was wonderful," said Puss. "They say you can change yourself into little things as small as a rat or a mouse. I do not think it is true. Can you show me?"

"Yes," roared the giant, "I can show you!" Then he changed himself into a mouse. And what do you think Puss did? *Zip!* She jumped on the mouse and ate him up, just like that.

Then she went to meet the King, and said, "Oh King, this is the castle of the rich Marquis of Carabas."

The King was pleased with the castle and with the land and with the young marquis. "This young man is a fine man to wed my daughter," said the King.

The king's daughter was happy to hear this, for she liked the young man very much.

So they were wed. The King stayed on a whole week at the castle. And Puss, and the master, and his wife were happy there ever after.

THE PIED PIPER OF HAMELIN

1

Hamelin is a little town in a country across the sea. Long ago a strange thing happened in Hamelin. A great many rats came into the town.

They were big, fierce rats. They chased the cats and dogs and scared the children. They ate the food on the tables. They ran up and down the streets in the daytime.

The Wise Men tried to think of a way to drive the rats out of the town. Cats and dogs could not do it, and the rats would not eat poison.

The Mayor said, "I wish I had a trap big and strong enough to catch the rats. I would give all my gold for it."

Just then there came a knock at the door. "Come in," said the Mayor.

The door opened and in came a very strange man. He was tall and thin, with bright blue eyes and light hair. His long coat was half of yellow and half of red. No one had ever seen him before.

The strange man went up to the Mayor and said, "I can drive the rats out of the town."

"Who are you," cried the Wise Men, "and how can you do this thing?"

"I am called the Pied Piper. I cannot tell you what I shall do. If you will promise to give me a thousand pieces of gold, I will soon show you."

"A thousand!" cried the Mayor. "I will give you five thousand if you can get rid of these rats!"

"No," said the Pied Piper, "a thousand is my fair price, and a thousand it shall be."

Then the Pied Piper went into the street. He took a pipe from his long coat and began to play a merry tune. Soon the rats came running from the houses.

Great rats, small rats, lean rats, brawny rats,
Brown rats, black rats, gray rats, tawny rats,
Grave old plodders, gay young friskers,
Fathers, mother, uncles, cousins,
Cocking tails, and pricking whiskers,
Families by tens and dozens,
Brothers, sisters, husbands, wives—
Followed the Piper for their lives.

The Piper walked slowly down the street, playing a merry tune, and the rats followed, dancing. They thought the music was about good things to eat. They forgot everything else as they ran after the Piper.

When they came to the river every rat danced into the water and was swept away. How happy the people were! They rang the bells and shouted for joy.

2

Then the Pied Piper said to the Mayor, "Now, if you please, I will take my thousand pieces of gold."

"A thousand pieces of gold!" cried the Mayor. "That is too much money. I will give you fifty."

"If you do not give me the money you will be sorry," said the strange man.

"You can do us no harm,"said the Mayor. "The rats are dead. You cannot bring them back."

Then the Pied Piper went into the street again. He played a few sweet notes on his pipe. At once the children came out of the houses.

All the little boys and girls,
With rosy cheeks and flowing curls,
And sparkling eyes and teeth like pearls,
Tripping and skipping ran merrily after
The wonderful music with shouting
    and laughter.

The Piper walked down the street and through the fields. When he reached the foot of the hill a door opened and he went in, still playing the beautiful tune.

All the children followed him and the door closed. One little boy, who was lame, could not run as fast as the other children. When the Mayor and the Wise Men came running up, they found him crying.

"Why do you cry?" said the Mayor.

"I wished to go with the other children," he said. "When the man played on his pipe it told us about a beautiful land. The sun was shining and the birds were singing. The children played in the fields. They were never ill nor lame. I ran as fast as I could, but when I came the children were gone, and I could not find the door."

The Mayor sent men north, south, east, and west to find the Piper. He said, "Tell him that I will give him all

the gold in the town if he will come back
and bring the children with him."

The fathers and mothers of Hamelin
waited and waited, but their little ones
did not come back.

All this was long ago, but no one
has ever seen the Piper or the little
children since.

If you go to Hamelin the
people will show you
the hill and the river.
You may walk down
Pied Piper street, but
you will hear no music.
No one is allowed to sing or play a tune on the street
down which the children followed the Pied Piper to the
land beyond the hills.

THE BELL OF ATRI

Long ago in Atri, there was a tower close beside the city gate. A great bell with a very long rope hung in this tower.

"This bell is for those in trouble," said the duke. "Even a child may ring it. When it rings, all Atri will come to help."

For many years the bell hung there, and very often it was rung. At last the rope was so badly worn that it broke.

In all Atri there was no rope long enough for this bell. "What shall we do?" cried the men. "Some one may need to ring this bell."

Then one looked at the grapevines that climbed over the tower. "Here is our new rope," he cried. He took the vines and twisted them until he made a long, strong rope. Then he fastened the rope to the bell.

That same day the bell was rung, and the people came running. They found no one there, but a horse was eating leaves from the new rope.

"Who rings the bell?" asked the duke.

"It is only a poor old white horse," said the people.

"Perhaps he needs help," said the duke. "Tell me about him."

"He belongs to the miser," said one. "When the horse was young, he carried his master on his back. Now that he is too old to do any work, his master gives him no food at all. He was eating leaves from the rope."

"Ah," said the duke, "he did very well to ring the Bell of Atri. Bring the miser to me."

The old miser was badly frightened when he was told to come to the duke, but he could not say no.

"Is this your horse?" asked the duke.

"He was once, but I really do not care for him now," said the miser.

The duke frowned and shook his head. "Give me your bag of gold," he said. "With this I shall build a warm stable. There your horse shall live in comfort for the rest of his life."

The miser looked around the place, but there was no one to help him. Very slowly he walked up to the duke and gave him the bag. Then he turned and went to his home. He knew that the duke was right. The old horse had rung the bell, and all Atri had come to help him.

Classics for Young Readers, Volume 2
Text Sources

Selections in this volume have been adapted from the following sources:

Aesop's Fables (pages 4-12) written by Lori Burgess

Child Life in Tale and Fable, A Second Reader, Etta Austin Blaisdell and Mary Frances Blaisdell (New York: The Macmillan Company, 1908)

The Elson Readers, Book One, William H. Elson and Lura E. Runkel (Chicago: Scott, Foresman and Company, 1920)

The Elson Readers, Book Two, William H. Elson and Lura E. Runkel (Chicago: Scott, Foresman and Company, 1920)

Everyday Classics, Second Reader, Franklin T. Baker, Ashley H. Thorndike, and Mildred Batchelder (New York: The Macmillan Company, 1922)

The Merrill Readers: Second Reader, Franklin B. Dyer and Mary J. Brady (New York: Charles E. Merrill Company, 1915)

The Natural Method Readers, A Second Reader, Hannah T. McManus and John H. Haaren (New York: Charles Scribner's Sons, 1915)

New American Readers, Horn-Shurter-Baugh, Book Two, Lila Baugh and Paul Whitfield Horn (Boston: Ginn and Company, 1918)

The Progressive Road to Reading, Book Two, Georgine Burchill, William L. Ettinger, and Edgar Dubs Shimer (New York: Silver, Burdett and Company, 1909)

Story Hour Readers, Book Two, Ida Coe and Alice J. Christie (New York: American Book Company, 1914)

Story Hour Readers Revised, Book Two, Ida Coe and Alice C. Dillon (New York: American Book Company, 1923)

Editor: John Holdren

Art Director: Steve Godwin

Designer: Elena López

Language Arts Advisor: Michele Josselyn

Illustrators:
Scott Brooks
Vince McGinley
Deborah Wolfe Ltd: (Jerry Dadds, Nancy Harrison, Jim Hays, Richard Hoit, Kelly Hume, Jeff LeVan, Richard Waldrep)

ISBN: 1-931728-01-1